KU-557-858

S00000912973

WILD BIOMES

ANIMALS OF THE ARCTIC TUNDRA

by Martha E. H. Rustad

raintree
a Capstone company — publishers for children

Raintree is an imprint of Capstone Global Library Limited, a company incorporated in England and Wales having its registered office at 264 Banbury Road, Oxford, OX2 7DY – Registered company number: 6695582

www.raintree.co.uk
myorders@raintree.co.uk

Edited by Jaclyn Jaycox
Designed by Hilary Wacholz
Original illustrations © Capstone Global Library Limited 2022
Picture research by Jo Miller
Production by Spencer Rosio
Originated by Capstone Global Library Ltd
Printed and bound in India

978 1 3982 2484 1 (hardback)
978 1 3982 2483 4 (paperback)

British Library Cataloguing in Publication Data
A full catalogue record for this book is available from the Britis

Acknowledgements
We would like to thank the following for permission to reproduce photographs: Alamy: FLPA, 14; Capstone: Eric Gohl, 5; iStockphoto: rpbirdman, 10; Shutterstock: AnnstasAg, 1, Daniel C Varming, 18, FloridaStock, 6, Gagat55, 11, GTW, 7, Jim Cumming, Cover, Jukka Jantunen, 8, Jukka Jantunen, 16, KeatsPhotos, 17, Maksimilian, 15, Modxka, 19, Nadya_Art, 21, nenets, 13, Paul Loewen, 9, Sergey Krasnoschokov, 12.
Design elements: Capstone; Shutterstock: AnnstasAg.

Contents

Words in **bold** are in the glossary.

THE ARCTIC TUNDRA

It's summer in the Arctic. The Sun never sets. Arctic animals use this time to raise babies. They eat lots of food. In the winter, the Sun never rises.

The Arctic sits in the far north. The tundra is a very dry, cold place. There is little snowfall. But most of the snow never melts. Rocks and small plants cover the ground. Many animals live in the tundra.

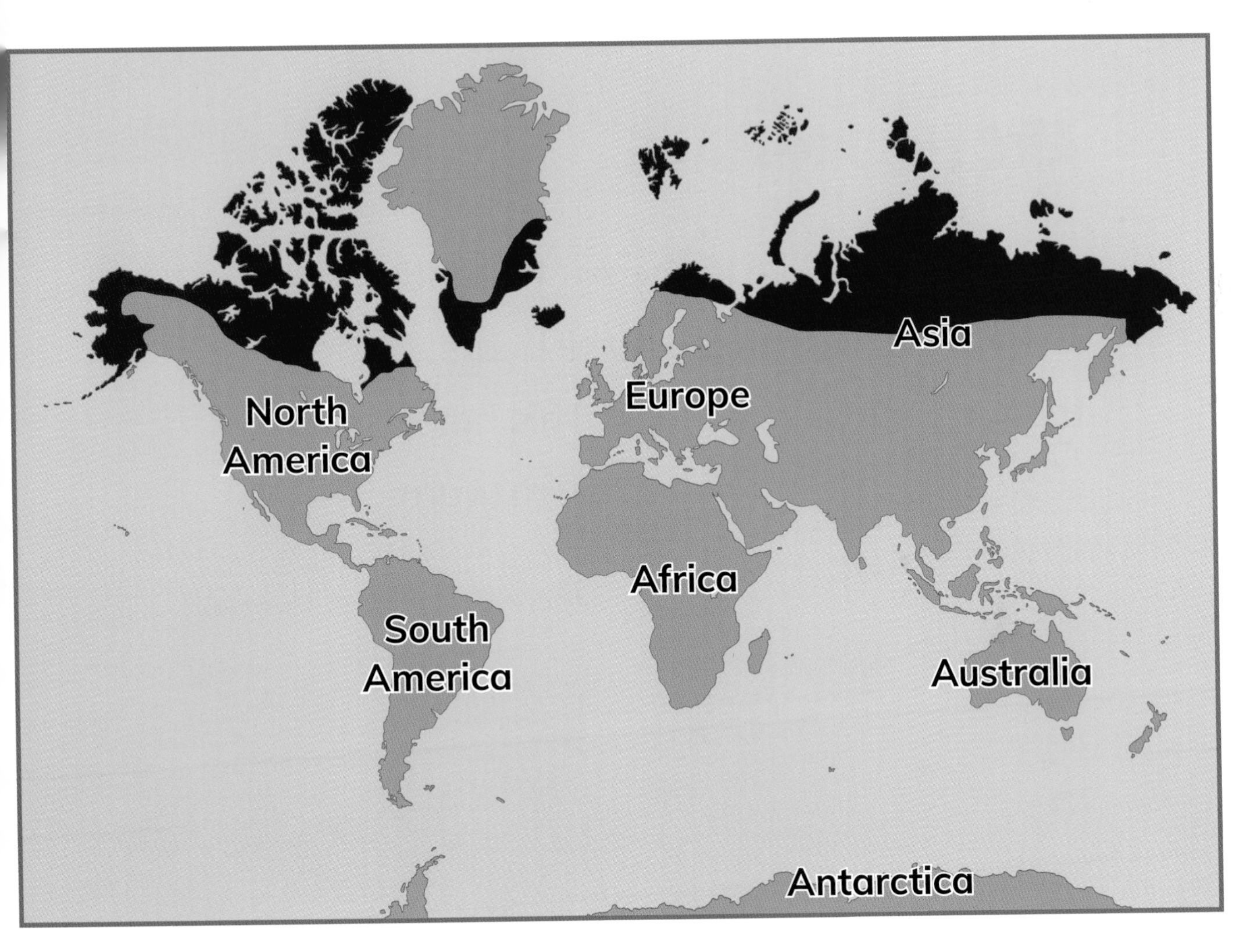
Asia
Europe
North America
Africa
South America
Australia
Antarctica

N
W
E
S
Arctic tundra

ARCTIC ANIMALS

Polar bears live in the Arctic tundra. Thick fur covers these huge bears. Under the fur, their skin is black. This helps them soak up sunlight to keep them warm.

White fur helps polar bears hide in the snow. These **predators** float on sea ice to find food. Polar bears hunt seals. Their noses smell **prey** under the ice. Sharp claws and teeth grab and tear their food.

Arctic hares nibble on tundra plants. Grey fur helps them hide from predators. They blend in with rocks. They use their long ears to listen out for danger. They escape using their long, powerful legs.

In the autumn, their fur changes. It turns white. They can hide in the snow. They use their sharp claws to dig for food under the snow and ice.

Snowy owls soar above the land. Their sharp eyes help them find prey. Strong claws help them grab mice, hares and **lemmings**. Sharp beaks tear their food. In winter, snowy owls listen for prey. They hear tiny animals hidden under the snow.

Groups of reindeer live in the tundra. During summer, they travel to the northern parts of the Arctic. They eat grasses and other plants. In winter, they move south. Branches and **mosses** are their winter food.

Strong legs carry them hundreds of kilometres. Their wide **hooves** help them walk in deep snow.

Not even Arctic animals can escape mosquitoes. Some mosquitoes live through winter. They have a special liquid in their bodies. It keeps them safe in freezing weather. They **thaw** in spring.

Female mosquitoes suck the blood of Arctic animals. They need the blood to lay eggs. Mosquito eggs hatch in spring. The young live near ponds and lakes. They grow quickly.

LIFE IN THE TUNDRA

Animals and plants in the tundra are part of a **food web**. Hares eat plants. Snowy owls eat hares. Many birds fly to the Arctic in the summer. They eat insects that hatch in warm weather. Arctic animals all need each other.

The Earth is getting warmer. It affects the Arctic. The ground thaws and the ice melts. Warm weather changes which plants grow well. Animals that eat some plants may no longer be able to find them.

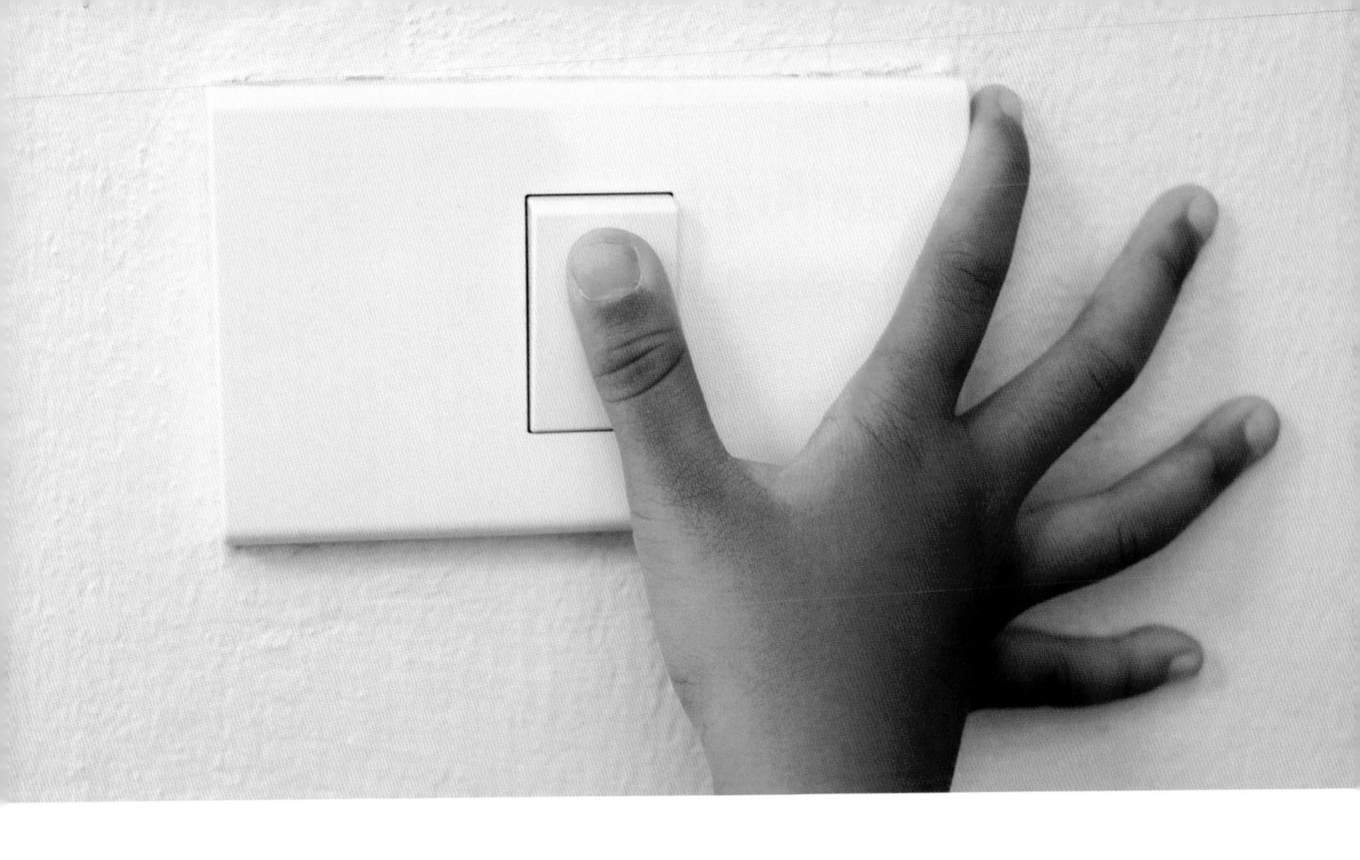

We can help save the planet. Walk more instead of going places by car. Turn off lights. Use less water. These things will help slow down **climate** change. We can protect the Arctic tundra and the animals that live there.

Hiding in the Arctic

Many Arctic tundra animals have white fur or feathers. Create your own Arctic landscape to see how these animals can hide.

What you'll need:

- white poster paper
- tape
- white card
- crayons or felt-tip pens
- drawings or print-outs of Arctic animals
- scissors

What you'll do:

1. Create an Arctic background. Use the white poster paper. This is your snowy land.

2. Add a few drawings of bushes or rocks. Attach a few snowballs made of crumpled pieces of white paper.
3. Draw pictures of Arctic animals on the cardboard, such as the ones below. Or print out photos from a computer. Cut out the animal from each picture.
4. Tape the animals onto your snowy land. Then stick the poster to a wall. Stand five steps back. How many animals can you see? Then stand 20 steps back. Now how many can you see?

Glossary

climate usual weather that occurs in a place

food web many food chains connected to one another

hoof hard covering on an animal's foot

lemming small mammal with furry feet and a short tail

moss soft, clumpy plant that usually grows in swamps and wetlands

predator animal that hunts and eats other animals for food

prey animal that is hunted by other animals for food

thaw become unfrozen

Find out more

Books

Food Webs (Life Science Stories), Leon Gray (Raintree, 2016)

Polar Bears Are Awesome (Polar Animals), Jaclyn Jaycox (Raintree, 2020)

Tundra Habitats Around the World (Exploring Earth's Habitats), Phillip Simpson (Raintree, 2020)

Websites

www.bbc.co.uk/bitesize/topics/z849q6f/articles/zvsp92p
The BBC Bitesize website has a fun video about biomes.

www.dkfindout.com/uk/animals-and-nature/habitats-and-ecosystems/tundra/
Learn more about tundras with DKfindout!

Index